If You're Thankful and You Know It

Chrissy Bozik

illustrated by
Patricia Storms

Scholastic Canada Ltd.
Toronto New York London Auckland Sydney
Mexico City New Delhi Hong Kong Buenos Aires

Scholastic Canada Ltd.
604 King Street West, Toronto, Ontario M5V 1E1, Canada

Scholastic Inc.
557 Broadway, New York, NY 10012, USA

Scholastic Australia Pty Limited
PO Box 579, Gosford, NSW 2250, Australia

Scholastic New Zealand Limited
Private Bag 94407, Botany, Manukau 2163, New Zealand

Scholastic Children's Books
Euston House, 24 Eversholt Street, London NW1 1DB, UK

www.scholastic.ca

Library and Archives Canada Cataloguing in Publication
Bozik, Chrissy, author
If you're thankful and you know it / Chrissy Bozik ; illustrated
by Patricia Storms.

ISBN 978-1-4431-5763-6 (softcover)

I. Storms, Patricia, illustrator II. Title.

PS8603.O9983I5 2017   jC813'.6   C2017-901450-1

6 5 4 3 2 1   Printed in Malaysia 108   17 18 19 20 21

I'm thankful for best friends, twins and love.
This book is for Glen, Karen and The Jimmer.
— C.B.

I am grateful, as always, for my Guido.
— P.S.

If the leaves are changing colours,
    jump right in!
If the leaves are changing colours,
    jump right in!
Rake them in a great big pile,
    dive in and play a while.
If the leaves are changing colours,
    jump right in!

If the air is getting chilly, bundle up!
If the air is getting chilly, bundle up!
Pull on your warmest sweater,
　and prepare for autumn weather.
If the air is getting chilly, bundle up!

If the geese are flying south,
   hear them honk!
If the geese are flying south,
   hear them honk!
They're flying in a V,
   leaving the snow for you and me.
If the geese are flying south,
   hear them honk!

If the trees are full of fruit, pick some apples!
If the trees are full of fruit, pick some apples!
Just climb right up the tree, and grab a Mac for me.
If the trees are full of fruit, pick some apples!

If you want to make a scarecrow, find a hat!
If you want to make a scarecrow, find a hat!
Stuff a shirt and pants,
  and really make him dance.
If you want to make a scarecrow,
  find a hat!

If you want to bake a pie, grab your cart!
If you want to bake a pie, grab your cart!
Head to the pumpkin patch,
  then bake your pie from scratch.
If you want to bake a pie, grab your cart!

If guests are coming over, give them hugs!
If guests are coming over, give them hugs!
Neighbours, friends and cousins,
    coming over by the dozens.
If guests are coming over, give them hugs!

If it's time for playing hockey, grab a stick!
If it's time for playing hockey, grab a stick!
Set up a game with friends,
  put a goalie at both ends.
If it's time for playing hockey, grab a stick!

If there's turkey on your plate, gobble it up!
If there's turkey on your plate, gobble it up!
A feast is really great, on this October date.
If there's turkey on your plate, gobble it up!

If you're thankful and you know it, shout hooray!
If you're thankful and you know it, shout hooray!
If you're thankful and you know it,
    and you really want to show it,
If you're thankful and you know it, shout hooray!